# LEARNING TOGETHER

## ADVICE AND INSTRUCTIONS ON COMPLETING THESE TESTS

1. There are 85 questions in each test. Make sure you have not missed a page.

2. Start at question 1 and work your way to question 85.

3. If you are unable to complete a question leave it and go to the next one.

4. Do not think about the question you have just left as this wastes time.

5. If you change an answer make sure the change is clear.

6. Make sure you spell correctly.

7. You may do any rough work on the test paper or on another piece of paper.

8. Each test should take approximately 50 minutes.

9. When you have finished each test mark it with an adult.

10. An adult may be able to explain any questions you do not understand.

# TEST 06

SCORE _____

1. Which letter appears once in TUMBLED but twice in RESTAURANT?　(＿＿＿＿＿＿)

2. Which letter appears once in ROMANTIC but not at all in FORMATION?　(＿＿＿＿＿＿)

3. Two times ten is the same as a number multiplied by four. What is the number?　(＿＿＿＿＿＿)

4. A banana and 2 apples cost 86p. Two bananas and 2 apples cost £1.16.
   How much is an apple?　(＿＿＿＿＿＿)

**In the questions below TWO words must change places so that the sentences make sense. Underline the TWO words that must change places.**

**Look at this example:　　The <u>wood</u> was made of <u>table</u>.**

5. The television was breakfast on after switched.

6. A car outside down broke the garage.

7. Take great care crossing when a busy road.

8. Not a pen I can without do my homework.

9. Making a foolish decision is sometimes hasty.

**The table below gives some information about the subtraction of numbers in the top row from numbers in the left hand column. Complete the table.**

| | — | 2.6 | | 4.9 |
|---|---|---|---|---|
| 10. | | | | |
| 11, 12. | 7.8 | | | 2.9 |
| 13, 14. | 5.3 | | 1.2 | |

In each question below write in the brackets a letter which will complete both the word in front of the brackets and the word after the brackets.

Look at this example.                                    **ROA (D) OOR**

15.      WIS    (   )  EAR          16. SEVE   (   )  ANGE          17. BOT  (   )  EIR

18.      SPEL   (   )  RACE         19.  TIC   (   )  ING

In each line below a word from the left-hand group joins one from the right-hand group to make a new word. The left-hand word comes first.
Underline the chosen words.

Look at this example.

| CORN | FARM | TIME | OVER | FIELD | YARD |
|------|------|------|------|-------|------|
| 20. STAR | ONLY | STIR | DEN | PAD | TING |
| 21. PACK | SPOKES | TOP | AGE | OVER | WHEEL |
| 22. TIN | CAP | BIN | BAG | GO | LID |
| 23. COT | MODEL | FOR | LED | RAT | RING |
| 24. UNDER | HOUSE | OPEN | FIRE | HOLD | OTHER |

Four children A, B, C and D sat a test in school. A scored 5 more marks than B and 8 less than C. D scored 37, which was 22 less than B scored.

How many marks did each child score?

25.  A scored        (_____)          26.  B scored  (_____)

27.  C scored        (_____)          28.  D scored  (_____)

In each of the following questions one word can be put in front of each of the four given words to form a new word. Write the correct word in the brackets.

Look at this example.

| | board | berry | out | bird | (BLACK) |
|---|---|---|---|---|---|
| 29. | take | stand | line | ground | (_____) |
| 30. | break | come | cry | burst | (_____) |
| 31. | table | less | keeper | piece | (_____) |
| 32. | ways | board | wards | light | (_____) |

Four brothers Alan, Bill, Chris and Don each own a car. Alan and Bill have sports cars and the others have hatchbacks. Bill and Don have new cars and the others own second-hand cars. Only the cars owned by Alan and Don have a radio.

33. Who has a new hatchback with a radio?  (_____)

34. Who has a hatchback which is not new and has no radio?  (_____)

35. Who has an old sports car with a radio?  (_____)

36. Has anyone a second-hand hatchback without a radio?  (_____)

37. Who has a new sports car without a radio?  (_____)

Complete each sequence by writing the correct number or numbers in the brackets.

| 38. | 3 | 4 | 6 | 10 | (_____) |
|---|---|---|---|---|---|
| 39. | 1.5 | 2.75 | 4 | 5.25 | (_____) |
| 40. | 100 | 64 | 36 | 16 | (_____) |
| 41. | 8.8 | 7.4 | 6 | 4.6 | (_____) |
| 42. | 520 | 432 | 344 | 256 | (_____) |
| 43. | (30,45) | (37,43) | (44,41) | (51,39) | (_____ , _____) |

In the following questions the letters of words have been jumbled up. A clue is given to help you find the word each time.

Look at this example:

| IATSDUM | Sports Ground | **STADIUM** |
|---------|---------------|-------------|

| | | | |
|---|---|---|---|
| 44. | AVRACAN | Mobile home | (_____) |
| 45. | TLAIOSHP | Where sick people are treated | (_____) |
| 46. | IELPMP | Small swelling on skin | (_____) |
| 47. | NGNILTHIG | Electrical storm | (_____) |
| 48. | SEVERER | Drive backwards | (_____) |
| 49. | ROAHCDR | Area where fruit trees grow | (_____) |

In the sentences below there are 5 words missing. From the lists A to E choose the MOST SUITABLE words to complete the sentences. Choose a word from list A to fill space A, a word from list B to fill space B and so on.

Underline the chosen word in each group.

Gasping for breath the runner made a ( A ) desperate ( B ) for the tape. ( C ) he collapsed ( D ) on the road, officials covered him with a blanket and then ( E ) him to a nearby hall.

| 50. A | 51. B | 52. C | 53. D | 54. E |
|-------|-------|-------|-------|-------|
| most | chase | Why | weary | sent |
| hopeful | go | Quickly | unconscious | pointed |
| great | spurt | But | tired | directed |
| last | bounce | As | over | ushered |
| big | fling | For | down | carried |

**The two sets of numbers on each line go together in a similar way. Write the missing number each time.**

Look at this example:     (7 → 14 → 16)     (9 → 18 → 20)     Double number and add 2

55.  (32 → 40 → 10)          ( 4 → 12 → __3__ )

56.  ( 3 → 9 → 27)          ( 5 → 25 → __125__ )

57.  (36 → 18 → 17)          (14 → 7 → __6__ )

58.  ( 5 → 7 → 49)          ( 9 → 11 → __121__ )

59.  ( 4 → 8 → 18)          ( 6 → 12 → __26__ )

**Two words inside the brackets have similar meanings to the words outside the brackets. Underline the two words each time.**

Look at this Example:        Horse,  Pig,    Cat        (Falcon, <u>Mouse</u>, Snake, Trout, <u>Badger</u>)

60.  Cabbage,   Turnip,    Carrot        (Cherry,  Wheat,  <u>Cauliflower</u>,  Pear,  <u>Parsnip</u>)

61.  Barrel,    Bucket,    Bath        (<u>Bottle</u>,  Basket,  Bag,  Box,  <u>Bowl</u>)

62.  Search,    Look,    Inquire        (Find,  <u>Seek</u>,  Report,  <u>Explore</u>,  Lead)

63.  Teach,    Educate,    Instil        (<u>Coach</u>,  Learn,  <u>Instruct</u>,  Study,  Swot)

64.  Vacant,    Free,    Available        (Unfurnished,  Occupied,  Fill,  <u>Empty</u>,  <u>Unoccupied</u>)

Some letters from the words in capitals have been used to make other words. Underline the TWO new words that have been made each time.

Look at this example:

| CONVENIENT | <u>Tonic</u> | Video | Notion | <u>Voice</u> |
|---|---|---|---|---|
| 65. PRACTICE | Erase | Trace | Create | Crate |
| 66. GLADIATOR | Tailor | Great | Tiger | Gloat |
| 67. DISCIPLE | Edits | Plaice | Slide | Piles |
| 68. OPERATION | Train | Rather | Parent | Nations |
| 69. MYSTERIOUS | Yeast | Mouse | South | Items |

RHOMBUS     TRAPEZIUM     PARALLELOGAM     RECTANGLE     KITE
The above are all quadrilaterals and are defined below.
Beside each definition write the name of the shape.

70.  The four sides are equal in length but the angles are not right angles.        (_____)

71.  Made up of 2 pairs of parallel lines. The opposite sides are equal and all the angles are right angles.        (_____)

72.  There are 2 pairs of equal sides which are not opposite to each other        (_____)

73.  A quadrilateral with one pair of sides parallel.        (_____)

74.  Opposite sides and angles equal. Two pairs of parallel lines.        (_____)

**The table below shows the number of pupils in a school who attended after-school activities.**

|  | Year 4 | Year 5 | Year 6 | Year 7 |
|---|---|---|---|---|
| Folk Dancing | 10 | 6 | 5 | 3 |
| Football + Hockey | 7 | 13 | 15 | 19 |
| Cookery | 6 | 8 | 5 | 8 |
| Choir | 7 | 5 | 6 | 4 |

75. Which activity becomes more popular as children get older?  (_____)

76. Which activity becomes less popular as children get older?  (_____)

77. Which activity is the second most popular?  (_____)

78. Which activity has exactly half as many taking part as another one has?  (_____)

79. It started to rain and all the football and hockey players were divided equally among the other clubs. How many were then at folk dancing?  (_____)

**In a number system**

| 1 | is written as | ~ \ | 2 | is written as | ~\~\ |
|---|---|---|---|---|---|
| 3 | is written as | >< | 4 | is written as | ><~\ |
| 6 | is written as | >< >< | 8 | is written as | >< >< ~\~\ |
| 10 | is written as | [] | | | |

**Which numbers are represented by the following?**

80. >< ><~\  (_____)     81. [] >< ~\~\  (_____)

82. [] >< >< ><  (_____)     83. [] [] >< >< ~\  (_____)

84. [] [] [] >< >< ~\~\  (_____)     85. [] [] [] [] [] ><~\~\  (_____)

# TEST 07

SCORE _____

1. Which letter occurs once in UTTERANCE, twice in THROUGHOUT and three times in AUGUSTUS? (_____)

2. Which letter, that does not occur in the word PRESENTABLE, occurs twice in DIMENSION? (_____)

3. What number is three times the half of 8 multiplied by six? (_____)

4. What is the difference between seven times nine and eight multiplied by five? (_____)

5. I get a total of 20 when I add half of 18 to a quarter of a certain number. What is that number? (_____)

**When completed the table below gives the answers when the numbers in the left-hand column are subtracted from the numbers in the top row.**

**Complete the table correctly.**

| – | 9.7 | 12.2 |
|---|---|---|
| 6. | 1.9 | 7.8 | |
| 7. 8. | 4.4 | | |
| 9. 10. | | 3.3 | |

In the questions below TWO words must change places so that the sentences make sense. Underline the TWO words that must change places.

**Look at this example:**     The <u>wood</u> was made of <u>table</u>.

11.   Many books can be learned from things.

12.   Swim only safe waters in.

13.   My uncle's brother is my nephew.

14.   Our the is at the end of school road.

15.   The runner fell lap in the last over.

In each question below write in the brackets a letter which will complete both the word in front of the brackets and the word after the brackets.

**Look at this example:**     ROA ( D ) OOR

16.   HAR ( ) ARLY      17. CRO ( ) ORD      18. POR ( ) ITE

19.   ARI ( ) YE      20. GRAS ( ) HASE      21. BE ( ) UST

In each line below a word from the left-hand group joins with one from the right-hand group to make a new word. The left-hand word comes first. Underline the chosen words.

**Look at this example:**     CORN   <u>FARM</u>   TIME        OVER   FIELD   <u>YARD</u>

22. SCAR     DOWN     OAR          TANG     SIDE     LET

23. OLD      UP       THIN         TEN      KING     DEN

24. ALL      UPPER    THEM         MOST     SELF     TOGETHER

25. PASS     IN       LET          TIME     PORT     ON

26. FAR      BE       FULL         AM       HIDE     WEAR

**£77.80 was made up using the smallest number of notes and coins shown below. How many of each were used?**

27. £10 notes    (_____)    28. £5 notes    (_____)    29. £1 coins    (_____)

30. 50p coins    (_____)    31. 20p coins    (_____)    32. 10p coins    (_____)


**Tom has more money than Jim and Paul, but less than Sid and Bob. Paul has less than Jim. Sid does not have the most money. List the 5 boys in order starting with the one who has the least money.**

(least) 33. (_____)    34. (_____)    35. (_____)    36. (_____)    37. (_____)    (most)


**In the following sentences the words in capital letters have been jumbled up. Re-arrange the letters to form the correct words.**

Look at this example:        **VESEN is a number.**        **(SEVEN)**

38. Mother is KNOWIRG in the kitchen.        (_____)

39. I like tea and toast for SAKRBEAFT        (_____)

40. Cartoons on OLETESIVIN are fun to watch.        (_____)

41. The chocolate SIUTBICS melted in the sun.    .    (_____)

42. The BILARRY received many new books.        (_____)

43. The boy played the EROCNT in the brass band.        (_____)

**In a certain month there were 5 Mondays and the 18th of the month was a Thursday.**

44. If there were 5 Wednesdays, what was the date of the last day of the month?  (_____)

45. What day was the 29th of the month?  (_____)

46. What was the date of the second Friday in the month?  (_____)

47. How many Tuesdays were there in the month?  (_____)

48. Which of the months April, June or August could it have been?  (_____)

**In each line below, the first word can be changed into the last word in three stages. Only one letter can be replaced at a time and proper words must be made each time.**

**Look at this example:**     tide     ( ride )     ( rode )     rope

49. dear     (_____)     (_____)     peep

50. lump     (_____)     (_____)     came

51. work     (_____)     (_____)     here

52. wood     (_____)     (_____)     hard

**Five children, Bob, Mike, Stan, Victor and Ken have a school bag each. Bob and Victor have leather bags and the others have canvas ones. Only Bob and Ken have bags with zips.**
**Stan and Bob have outside and inside pockets in their bags. The others have only inside pockets.**

53. Who has a leather bag with a zip? ( _____ )

54. What is the bag with an outside pocket and no zip made of? ( _____ )

55. Who has a canvas bag with a zip and no outside pockets? ( _____ )

56. Who has a canvas bag with no zip but with a full set of pockets? ( _____ )

57. How many children have bags that are not canvas, have no zips
and have inside pockets? ( _____ )

**Complete the following sequences. The alphabet is printed to help you.**

A B C D E F G H I J K L M N O P Q R S T U V W X Y Z

58. C1F      D3G      E5H      F7I      ( _____ )

59. CX       FW       IV       LU       ( _____ )

60. Y        W        T        P        ( _____ )

61. PBZ      OCY      NDX      MEW      ( _____ )

62. Z        X        V        T        ( _____ )

63. BAC      EDF      HGI      KJL      ( _____ )

In each of the following questions, the numbers in the second column are formed from the numbers in the first column. A different rule is used for each question.

Write your answers in the brackets.

64.  4 ⟶ 15
     6 ⟶ 35
     8 ⟶ 63
     10 ⟶ (__99__)

65.  23 ⟶ 12
     35 ⟶ 18
     49 ⟶ 25
     55 ⟶ (__28__)

66.  4 ⟶ 6
     6 ⟶ 9
     10 ⟶ 15
     12 ⟶ (__18__)

67.  144 ⟶ 14
     100 ⟶ 12
     81 ⟶ 11
     36 ⟶ (__8__)

In each line below there are 3 words which change by following a rule.
Find the rule for each line and write the missing word.

Look at this Example:   NOT - TON        LIVE - EVIL       STOP - POTS

68.  hasten  -  net        header    -  red       jersey    -  (__yes__)

69.  cartridge - cage       elapse    -  else      figure    -  (__fire__)

70.  surge   -  sure        tenant    -  tent      existent  -  (__exit__)

71.  notable -  tale        impassive -  pave      mediaeval -  (__dial__)

72.  digger  -  dire        dowse     -  does      formula   -  (__foal__)

Complete the statements below by writing your answers on the lines.

73.  (67 x 15) + (67 x 3) = 67 x (__18__)

     If 204 ÷ 12 = 17 then

74.  (12 x 17) + (__11__) = 215

In a code **SLITHER** is written as **ABCDEFG** and **POUCH** is written as **HIJKE**.

Which words are represented by the following code words?

75. EIJAF      ( HOUSE )      76. DCBFA    ( TILES )

77. HCDKEFG      ( PITCHER )      78. DEGCKF   ( THRICE )

Write the following words in code.

79. COURSE      ( IIJGAF )      80. LEISURE   ( BFCAJGF )

Using the numbers 2, 4, 6 and 7 ONCE ONLY in each question, fill in the spaces in a way that will make the statements correct.

Look at this example:      ( 2 + 4 ) + ( 6 + 7 ) = 19

81. ( ___ + ___ ) X ( ___ + ___ ) = 90

82. ( ___ – ___ ) + ( ___ – ___ ) = 3

83. ( ___ X ___ ) ÷ ( ___ – ___ ) = 8

84. ( ___ X ___ ) – ( ___ X ___ ) = 16

85. ( ___ + ___ + ___ ) X ( ___ ) = 34

# TEST 08

SCORE _____

1. Which letter occurs once in HEADINGS and twice in THOUGHTS? (_____)

2. Which letter occurs twice in PHOTOGRAPHIC and once in INHARMONIOUS? (_____)

3. Which letter occurs once in HOUSEHOLD, twice in MALADJUSTED
   and thrice in DIVIDENDS? (_____)

**In the questions below TWO words must change places so that the sentences make sense. Underline the TWO words that must change places.**

**Look at this example:**     The <u>wood</u> was made of <u>table</u>.

4. The difficult asked a teacher question.

5. Thunder sound of the made me jump.

6. A cat dog's into the raced kennel.

7. Book pages are missing from the five.

8. Television is to very boring sometimes watch.

9. It's sleep for bed and time for time.

**In each question below write in the brackets a letter which will complete both the word in front of the brackets and the word after the brackets.**

**Look at this example.**          **ROA (D) OOR**

10.   HU   (  )  ORE          11.   SIL   (  )  ILT

12.   HUR   (  )  ACE          13.   STAR   (  )  TEM

14.  PART   (  )  ULE          15.   LAS   (  )  ERD

The table below gives some information about the addition of numbers in the left hand column to numbers in the top row.

Complete the table.

| + | 7.5 | | 3.5 |
|---|---|---|---|
| 3.8 | | 4.2 | |
| 5.6 | | | 9.1 |

16.
17. 18.
19. 20.

In the brackets, write the numbers required to complete the statements correctly.

21. (_____)  +  19  =  45

22. 396  −  7  =  (_____)

23. 5  X  45  =  5  X  (_____)  +  (5  X  6)

24. 12  X  (_____)  =  6  X  124

25. 39  X  16  =  (_____)  +  (39  X  15)

In each of the following words there are 4 successive letters which make a new word. Write the new word in the brackets.

Look at this Example: **PLENTIFUL ( LENT )**

26. CUPBOARD (_____)    27. FOREARM (_____)    28. SHIVER (_____)

29. BADMINTON (_____)    30. GAUNTLET (_____)    31. ATMOSPHERE (_____)

32. YEARNED (_____)

In the sentences below there are 5 words missing. From the lists A to E choose the MOST SUITABLE words to complete the sentences. Choose a word from list A to fill space A, a word from list B to fill space B and so on. Underline the chosen word in each group.

The first ( A ) in the book was rather ( B ) but as the story ( C ) things became more exciting. The hero ( D ) the ( E ) damsel and finally married her.

| 33. A | 34. B | 35. C | 36. D | 37. E |
|---|---|---|---|---|
| pages | excited | went | fought | young |
| sentences | interesting | developed | imprisoned | only |
| chapter | bad | shows | saw | helpless |
| part | boring | continues | rescued | evil |
| story | short | unfolds | met | capture |

At one time £1.00 was worth 224 Japanese yen.

38. How many yen would £2.50 have been worth?    (_____ Yen )

39. How many yen would £4.25 have been worth?    (_____ Yen )

40. In British money what was the value of 392 yen?    (_ £ _____)

41. In British money what was the value of 672 yen?    (_ £ _____)

In the following questions the letters of words have been jumbled up. A clue is given to help you find the word each time.

Look at this Example:    IATSDUM   **Sports Ground**   <u>**STADIUM**</u>

42.  IGNEPUN      Flightless sea bird                                (_____)

43.  HDUSOLRE    Joint at top of arm                                (_____)

44.  INVSRAH      Liquid which gives glossy appearance to wood   (_____)

45.  NAMHELO      Opening in floor/sewer etc for person to pass through  (_____)

46.  CKUKSACR    Walker's bag worn on the back                    (_____)

47.  LFTIFAHU     To be loyal and true                               (_____)

48.  INCEDEVE    Information collected by police after a crime    (_____)

**One year February started and ended on the same day.**
**The 7th of the month was a Wednesday.**

49.  How many Thursdays were there in the month?        (_____)

50.  What was the date of the third Tuesday?            (_____)

51.  What day was the 19th of February?                (_____)

52.  What date was the last Saturday in January?        (_____)

53.  What date was the second Tuesday in March?      (_____)

**In the questions below give the next number in each series.**

54.     3          4          7          12          (_____)

55.     2          6          18          54          (_____)

56.   21.5       17        12.5         8           (_____)

57.   8.8        8.2        7.6         7.0          (_____)

58.   4.83      5.34       5.85        6.36         (_____)

**A child emptied her money box and had the following coins; four £1 coins, seven 50p coins, twelve 20p coins, nineteen 10p coins, fourteen 5p coins.**

59.  What was the total amount of money?          (_£_____)

60.  How much more would she need to buy a toy at £15.99?          (_£_____)

61.  By how much did the value of the 20p coins exceed the
     value of the 5p coins?          (_£_____)

62.  Would it have been possible to change the coins of lesser
     value than 50p to an exact number of £1 coins?          (_____)

| Number of children | ? | 15 | 8 | 6 | 2 | 1 |
|---|---|---|---|---|---|---|
| Number of pets kept by each child | 0 | 1 | 2 | 3 | 4 | 5 |

**The table above shows the results of a survey on the pets kept by 40 children.**

63.  How many children kept no pets?          (_____)

64.  How many children with pets kept less than 3?          (_____)

65.  How many children kept more than 3 pets?          (_____)

66.  What fraction of the children did not keep pets?          (_____)

**In each question below a boy ALWAYS STARTS OFF facing NORTH WEST. (NW)**

67. In what direction is he facing if he makes a quarter turn anti-clockwise?　　(_____)

68. In what direction is he facing if he makes a three-quarter turn clockwise?　　(_____)

69. In what direction is he facing if he makes a quarter turn anti-clockwise
    and then a half turn clockwise?　　(_____)

70. In what direction is he facing if he makes a three-quarter turn clockwise and
    a half turn clockwise, and finally a quarter turn anti-clockwise?　　(_____)

**In each of the following questions one word can be put in front of each of the four given words to form a new word. Write the correct word in the brackets.**

**Look at this example:**　　**board**　　**berry**　　**out**　　**bird**　　**(BLACK)**

71. mill　　fall　　shield　　screen　　(_____)

72. shot　　less　　thirsty　　shed　　(_____)

73. card　　man　　mark　　master　　(_____)

74. age　　hole　　kind　　slaughter　　(_____)

75. scape　　mark　　lord　　slide　　(_____)

The table below gives the time in seconds taken by 4 children to swim distances of 1, 2 and 5 lengths of a swimming pool.

| No of LENGTHS | 1 | 2 | 5 |
|---|---|---|---|
| TOM | 23sec | 59sec | 218sec |
| BETTY | 34sec | 85sec | 315sec |
| SIMON | 28sec | 70sec | 256sec |
| RUTH | 32sec | 81sec | 289sec |

76. Which child swam 5 lengths the quickest?　　　　　(_____)

77. Which child took approximately 10 times as long to swim
5 lengths as Simon took to swim 1 length?　　　　　(_____)

78. For which child was the difference in time for swimming
1 length and 2 lengths the greatest?　　　　　(_____)

79. For which child was the difference in time for swimming
1 length and 5 lengths the least?　　　　　(_____)

**Six girls A, B, C, D, E and F stand in a straight line.**

**Neither A nor B is at the end of the line.**
**No one is further right than C.**
**E is beside neither C nor A.**
**D is beside E and B**
**F is one of the girls in the middle.**

**List the girls in order.**

**LEFT**　80. (____)　81. (____)　82. (____)　83. (____)　84. (____)　85. (____) **RIGHT**

# TEST 09

SCORE _____

1. Which letter occurs once in the word GEOGRAPHY and twice in the word GEOMETRY? (__________)

2. Which letter occurs three times in the word FLUORESCENCE and once in the word BEAUTY? (__________)

3. Which letter occurs most often in the word BELLIGERENT? (__________)

4. If I add 8 to a certain number I get an answer which is 4 less than 28. What is the number? (__________)

5. Jane and Sally had 31 comics between them. Jane had 9 more than Sally. How many comics did Sally have? (__________)

**In the questions below TWO words must change places so that the sentences make sense. Underline the TWO words that must change places.**

**Look at this example:** **The <u>wood</u> was made of <u>table</u>.**

6. The did you go to why park?

7. The its ate all of horse oats.

8. Out the door opened the cat ran when.

9. There are a basket of apples in the lot.

10. He into the bicycle rode the wall.

11. Eat down now and sit up your dinner.

**The table below gives some information about the addition of numbers in the left hand column to numbers in the top row. Complete the table.**

| | | | | |
|---|---|---|---|---|
| 12. | + | 0.9 | 2.1 | |
| 13. 14. | 6.8 | | | 8.7 |
| 15. 16. | 4.1 | | 6.2 | |

In each question write in the brackets one letter which will complete both the word in front of the brackets and the word after the brackets.

Look at this example:          ROA (D) OOR

17.   BEL   (   )   ELL.          18.  DUC   (   )   ICK.          19.   FEA   (   )   ING.

20.   ITC   (   )   EAR.          21.  EXI   (   )   ALE.          22.  CLEA   (   )   URAL.

Arrange the following words in alphabetical order.

**PUPPY   POETRY   POCKET   POPPY   POPPET.**

First                                                                                          Last

23.   (_____)          24. (_____)          25. (_____)          26. (_____)          27. (_____)

In the following questions a letter can be taken from the first word and put into the second word to form TWO new words.

Write both NEW words.

Look at this example:  THEN   TANK     ( TEN )    ( THANK )

28.  GAVEL          SING          (_____)          (_____)

29.  FOUND          BOY          (_____)          (_____)

30.  SHORT          BEAD          (_____)          (_____)

31.  DETER          SING          (_____)          (_____)

32.  FLOAT          SHUT          (_____)          (_____)

33.  RINSE          SAIL          (_____)          (_____)

34.  TITLE          SACK          (_____)          (_____)

Complete the following sequences. The alphabet is printed to help you.

A B C D E F G H I J K L M N O P Q R S T U V W X Y Z

| | | | | | | | |
|---|---|---|---|---|---|---|---|
| 35. | EN | FO | GP | HQ | | | ( IR ) |
| 36. | A | E | I | M | Q | U | ( Y ) |
| 37. | A | C | F | H | K | M | ( P ) |
| 38. | BZB | EXE | HVH | KTK | | | ( NRN ) |
| 39. | CAB | FDE | IGH | LJK | | | ( OMN ) |
| 40. | WAC | EBU | SCG | IDQ | | | ( OEK ) |

**The dates of birth of 4 friends are:**

**Tim   19.10.91          Paul   3.8.92          Roy   17.2.91          Bob   12.3.92**

41.  Who is the oldest?                                    ( Roy )

42.  Whose birthday is nearest to Easter?         ( Bob )

43.  How old was Tim on 19.10.98?                    ( 7 )

44.  In which year did Roy have his 6th birthday?   ( 1997 )

45.  What age was Bob on 12th September 1999?    ( 7 )

**In the sentences below there are 5 words missing. From the lists A to E choose the MOST SUITABLE words to complete the sentences. Choose a word from list A to fill space A, a word from list B to fill space B and so on.**

**Underline the chosen word in each group.**

Many ( A ) can be planted in the spring. They need to be carefully ( B ) to help germination. Moisture and heat are ( C ) for growth. ( D ) light will ( E ) the growth of young shoots and weaken the plants.

| 46. A | 47. B | 48. C | 49. D | 50. E |
|-------|-------|-------|-------|-------|
| plant | watch | helpful | Weak | help |
| flower | moved | essential | Plentiful | encourage |
| seeds | observe | bad | Sun | cause |
| things | examined | harmful | Insufficient | hamper |
| vegetables | tended | useful | Extra | develop |

**The information below is about 4 boys A, B, C and D and the hobbies they enjoy.**
**A and B are the only two who like both reading and football.**
**B and D are the only two who like both football and painting.**
**C and A are the only two who like both stamp collecting and cycling.**

51. Who likes football but not painting?                    (_____)

52. Who likes cycling but not football?                      (_____)

53. Which hobby does A not have?                             (_____)

54. Which footballer paints and reads?                       (_____)

55. Which cyclist collects stamps but does not read?         (_____)

56. Which hobby is the most popular?                         (_____)

In each line below, the first word can be changed into the last word in three stages. Only one letter can be replaced at a time and proper words must be made each time.

Look at this example:          tide          ( ride )          ( rode )          rope

57.  time          (_____)          (_____)          lane

58.  weir          (_____)          (_____)          team

59.  pack          (_____)          (_____)          rice

60.  pint          (_____)          (_____)          lane

61.  work          (_____)          (_____)          load


The two sets of numbers on each line go together in a similar way. Write the missing number each time.

Look at this example:          (3 → 27 → 23)          (5 → 125 → 121)

(Cube number and subtract 4)


62.  ( 81 → 9 → 7 )                    ( 25 → 5 → _____ )

63.  ( 12 → 24 → 30 )              ( 16 → 32 → _____ )

64.  ( 7 → 49 → 50 )                ( 11 → 121 → _____ )

65.  ( 72 → 36 → 33 )              ( 40 → 20 → _____ )

66.  ( 4 → 16 → 21 )                ( 6 → 36 → _____ )

67.  ( 15 → 30 → 20 )              ( 22 → 44 → _____ )

**£43.75 was made up using the smallest number of notes and coins shown below.
How many of each were used?**

68. £5 notes    (_____)     69. £1 coins    (_____)     70. 20p coins    (_____)

71. 2p coins    (_____)     72. 1p coins    (_____)

Some letters from the words in capitals have been used to make other words. Underline the TWO
new words that have been made each time.

| Look at this example: | **CONVENIENT** | <u>tonic</u> | video | notion | <u>voice</u> |
|---|---|---|---|---|---|
| 73. PENINSULA | please | slain | usual | pulse | |
| 74. GEOGRAPHY | grape | prayer | repay | repair | |
| 75. RESEARCHED | chase | dream | scarce | heard | |
| 76. MANIPULATE | pulse | tulip | lament | altar | |
| 77. AMBULANCE | blame | learn | manila | uncle | |
| 78. CATASTROPHE | castle | roast | treat | stream | |
| 79. SAFEGUARD | feast | garage | feuds | urges | |

**The following questions are about the numbers in the diagram.**

80.  Which number is in both the circle and square but
     not in the triangle?

     (_____)

81.  Which numbers are in both the circle and triangle
     but not in the square?

     (_____)

82.  Which numbers appear in all three figures?

     (_____)

83.  Find the sum of all the numbers which appear
     in one figure only.          (_____)

84.  Take the sum of the numbers that are in the square, but not the triangle,
     from the sum of the numbers that are in the circle but not the square.     (_____)

85.  Take the sum of the numbers that are in the circle, but not the triangle
     or square, from the sum of the numbers that are in the triangle,
     but not the circle or square.          (_____)

# TEST 10

SCORE _____

1. Which letter occurs twice in SUPPOSITION, once in SUPPOSE and not at all in SUPPER? (_____)

2. Which letter occurs once in BEDROOM and twice in MOMENTARY? (_____)

3. Which letters occur twice as often in BELONGINGS as in the word SONGS? (_____)

4. When I subtract 7 from a certain number the answer is $\frac{1}{5}$ of 35. What is the number? (_____)

5. Lucy has 3 times as many balloons as Mary and half as many as Pat who has 12 balloons. If Lucy gave 2 of her balloons to Mary and Pat gave 1 to Mary, how many would Mary then have? (_____)

**In the questions below TWO words must change places so that the sentences make sense. Underline the TWO words that must change places.**

**Look at this example:** **The <u>wood</u> was made of <u>table</u>.**

6. Do not from pages tear the books.

7. The girls park their bicycles to the rode.

8. The lights could and we fused not see.

9. May I door you to the see?

10. Curly pigs have most tails.

11. The teacher books the marked in school.

The table below gives some information about the subtraction of numbers in the top row from numbers in the left hand column

Complete the table.

| | | | |
|---|---|---|---|
| 12. | — | 3.1 | |
| 13. 14. | | 8.2 | |
| 15. | 4.9 | | 2.1 |
| 16. 17. | 6.5 | | |

In each question write in the brackets one letter which will complete both the word in front of the brackets and the word after the brackets.

Look at this example:     ROA (D) OOR

18.   SIL   (_____) ISS

19.   BOR   (_____) ARN

20.   MINU   (_____) IGN

21.   HEI   (_____) EADY

22.   DUS   (_____) IRED

23.   MEN   (_____) SED

In each line below a word from the left-hand group joins one from the right-hand group to make a new word. The left-hand word comes first.
Underline the chosen words.

Look at this example:     CORN     __FARM__     TIME          OVER     FIELD     __YARD__

| | | | | | | |
|---|---|---|---|---|---|---|
| 24. CUT | BOW | PIT | | LED | TEN | CHAIR |
| 25. GO | MAT | CAN | | DYE | AT | SHALL |
| 26. CUE | ARM | PAD | | ILL | BIT | OUR |
| 27. COY | CURE | OR | | BIT | TONE | FEW |
| 28. AN | ME | DOE | | NINE | ERR | AN |
| 29. PIE | SEAL | LINE | | PIPE | BALD | THRONE |

In the following questions a letter can be taken from the first word and put into the second word to form TWO new words. Write both NEW words.

Look at this example:  THEN    TANK       ( TEN )    ( THANK )

The H moves from THEN to TANK and makes the new words TEN and THANK

30.  TIRE          HEAD          (_____)          (_____)

31.  SWERVE        TIN           (_____)          (_____)

32.  HOST          EVEN          (_____)          (_____)

33.  FRIGHT        HOSE          (_____)          (_____)

34.  BELOW         FRIGHT        (_____)          (_____)

35.  BEAD          POT           (_____)          (_____)

In each line below there are 3 pairs of words which change by following a rule.
Find the rule for each line and write the missing word.

Look at this example:          NOT - TON          LIVE - EVIL          STOP <u>POTS</u>
The letters are reversed to give a new word.

36.  patrol - tap          bustle - sub          nibble -          (_____)

37.  cheap - pea           abate - eat           backcloth -      (_____)

38.  gravel - leg          nectar - ran          bachelor -       (_____)

39.  swath - sat           graph - gap           phantom -        (_____)

40.  forget - ore          clout - lot           chapter  -       (_____)

**Two words inside the brackets have similar meanings to the words outside the brackets. Underline the TWO words each time.**

Look at this Example:    horse,    pig,    cat    (falcon, <u>mouse</u>, snake, trout, <u>badger</u>)

41.  shoe, sandal, boot        (feet, trainers, walk, wellingtons, socks)

42.  steam, poach, boil        (fish, fry, cook, roast, vegetables)

43.  candle, lamp, sun         (burn, torch, mirror, match, shine)

44.  sad, gloomy, melancholy   (unhappy, dreamy, tired, content, dreary)

45.  daffodil, tulip, daisy    (garden, iris, beech, rose, cauliflower)

**£69.64 was made up using the smallest number of notes and coins shown below.
How many of each were used?**

46.  £10 notes    (_____)    47.  £5 notes  (_____)         48.  £1 coins    (_____)

49.  20p coins    (_____)    50.  2p coins  (_____)

**Five children A, B, C, D and E went to school. B arrived punctually.
D arrived after B but before A. C arrived early. E was last to arrive.**

51.  Who arrived at school at the right time?      (_____)

52.  How many arrived after C?                      (_____)

53.  How many were late for school?                 (_____)

54.  How many arrived before A?                      (_____)

55.  How many arrived before D?                      (_____)

In each of the following questions the word outside the brackets must ALWAYS HAVE one of the things inside the brackets.

Underline one word only inside the bracket.

Look at this example:          A MAN always has  (wife,  job, car,  <u>head</u>,  children)

56.  A HOUSE always has          (stairs,  garage,  roof,  garden)

57.  A CANAL always has          (barge,  locks,  water,  holiday-makers)

58.  A TRAIN always has          (passengers,  cargo,  engine,  driver)

59.  A BOY always has          (shoes,  limbs,  bicycle,  sister)


**In a certain month there were 5 Thursdays. The 16th of the month was a Wednesday.**

60.  How many Tuesdays were there in the month?          (_____)

61.  What day was the 1st of the month?          (_____)

62.  What date was the second Friday?          (_____)

63.  Which of these months could it be ?          APRIL, JANUARY, JUNE **(underline one)**

64.  How many Sundays are there in the next month?          (_____)


**Amy, Beth, Carol, Dot and Edith each have a new dress.**
**Amy, Beth and Dot have pink dresses, the others have green ones.**
**Only Carol and Dot have dresses with belts.**
**Beth and Edith have cotton dresses and the others have linen ones.**

65.  Who has a pink dress with a belt?          (_____)

66.  Who has a green cotton dress?          (_____)

67.  Whose green dress has no belt?          (_____)

68.  Who has a pink cotton dress without a belt?          (_____)

69.  Whose linen dress has no belt?          (_____)

In each line below the first word can be changed into the last word in three stages. Only one letter can be altered at a time and proper words must be made each time.

Look at this example:　　　　　tide　　( ride )　　( rode )　　rope

70. farm　　(＿＿＿＿)　　(＿＿＿＿)　　word

71. lime　　(＿＿＿＿)　　(＿＿＿＿)　　tale

72. many　　(＿＿＿＿)　　(＿＿＿＿)　　nine

73. sand　　(＿＿＿＿)　　(＿＿＿＿)　　bunk

74. hard　　(＿＿＿＿)　　(＿＿＿＿)　　cafe

75. lose　　(＿＿＿＿)　　(＿＿＿＿)　　fast

In the following questions the numbers in the second column are formed from the numbers in the first column by using a certain rule. Put the correct answer opposite the arrow.

76. 1 $\longrightarrow$ 2　　　77. 2 $\longrightarrow$ 13　　78. 24 $\longrightarrow$ 10

2 $\longrightarrow$ 9　　　　　5 $\longrightarrow$ 31　　　　36 $\longrightarrow$ 14

3 $\longrightarrow$ 28　　　　6 $\longrightarrow$ 37　　　　42 $\longrightarrow$ 16

4 $\longrightarrow$ (＿＿)　　7 $\longrightarrow$ (＿＿)　　60 $\longrightarrow$ (＿＿)

79. 9 $\longrightarrow$ 4　　　80. 1 $\longrightarrow$ 4　　81. 24 $\longrightarrow$ 42

36 $\longrightarrow$ 7　　　　3 $\longrightarrow$ 14　　　36 $\longrightarrow$ 63

64 $\longrightarrow$ 9　　　　4 $\longrightarrow$ 19　　　47 $\longrightarrow$ 74

81 $\longrightarrow$ (＿＿)　　5 $\longrightarrow$ (＿＿)　　68 $\longrightarrow$ (＿＿)

**The graph below represents the journey made by a motorist one day.**

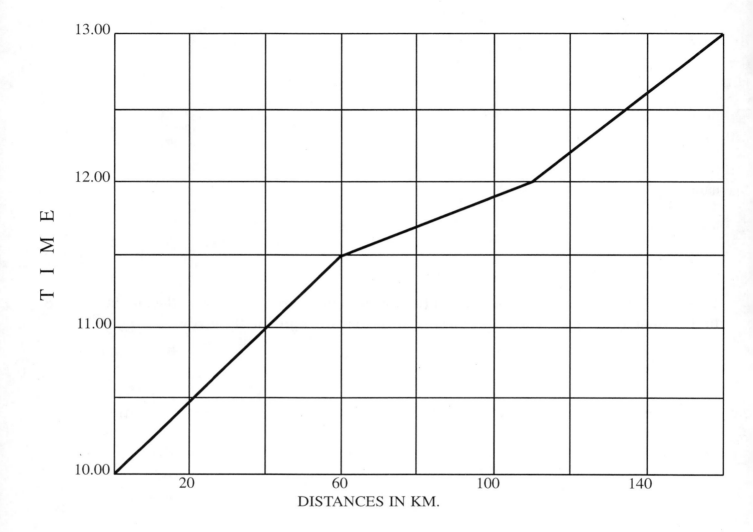

82. How far had he driven by 11.00 in the morning?          (_____km)

83. What was his average speed from 10.00 to 11.30?          (_____km/h)

84. How much of the journey did he still have to do at 11.30?          (_____km)

85. Part of the journey was along a fast motorway.
    At what time did he leave the motorway?          (_____o'clock)

Answers to Test 06

1. T
2. C
3. 5
4. 28p
5. BREAKFAST  SWITCHED
6. OUTSIDE  BROKE
7. CROSSING  WHEN
8. NOT  WITHOUT
9. FOOLISH  HASTY
10. 4.1
11. 5.2
12. 3.7
13. 2.7
14. 0.4
15. H or P
16. R
17. H
18. T
19. K
20. STAR  TING
21. PACK  AGE
22. BIN  GO
23. MODEL  LED
24. HOUSE  HOLD
25. 64
26. 59
27. 72
28. 37
29. UNDER
30. OUT
31. TIME
32. SIDE
33. DON
34. CHRIS
35. ALAN
36. YES
37. BILL
38. 18
39. 6.5
40. 4
41. 3.2
42. 168
43. 58, 37
44. CARAVAN
45. HOSPITAL
46. PIMPLE
47. LIGHTNING
48. REVERSE
49. ORCHARD
50. LAST
51. SPURT
52. AS
53. UNCONSCIOUS
54. CARRIED
55. 3 (X+8) ÷ 4
56. 125 (X CUBED)
57. 6         (X÷2) − 1
58. 121       (X+2) SQ
59. 22        2X+10
60. CAULIFLOWER, PARSNIP
61. BOTTLE BOWL
62. SEEK EXPLORE
63. COACH INSTRUCT
64. EMPTY UNOCCUPIED
65. TRACE CRATE
66. GLOAT TAILOR
67. SLIDE PILES
68. TRAIN PARENT
69. MOUSE ITEMS
70. RHOMBUS
71. RECTANGLE
72. KITE
73. TRAPEZIUM
74. PARALLELOGRAM
75. F.BALL + HOCKEY
76. FOLK DANCING
77. COOKERY
78. COOKERY
79. 42
80. 7
81. 15
82. 19
83. 27
84. 38
85. 55

Answers to Test 07

1. U
2. I
3. 72
4. 23
5. 44
6. 10.3
7. 5.3
8. 7.8
9. 6.4
10. 5.8
11. BOOKS  THINGS
12. ONLY  IN
13. BROTHER  NEPHEW
14. THE  SCHOOL
15. LAP  OVER
16. E
17. W
18. K
19. D
20. P
21. D or G
22. SCAR  LET
23. THIN  KING
24. UPPER  MOST
25. PASS  PORT
26. BE  AM
27. 7
28. 1
29. 2
30. 1
31. 1
32. 1
33. PAUL
34. JIM
35. TOM
36. SID
37. BOB
38. WORKING
39. BREAKFAST
40. TELEVISION
41. BISCUITS
42. LIBRARY
43. CORNET
44. 31st
45. MONDAY
46. 12th
47. 5
48. AUGUST
49. PEAR  PEER *
50. LAMP  CAMP *
51. WORE  WERE *
52. WORD  WARD *
53. BOB
54. CANVAS
55. KEN
56. STAN
57. 1
58. G9J
59. OT
60. K
61. LFV
62. R
63. NMO
64. 99   X SQUARED − 1
65. 28   (X+1)÷2
66. 18   1½X
67. 8    SQ ROOT X + 2
68. YES
69. FIRE
70. EXIT
71. DIAL
72. FOAL
73. 18
74. 11
75. HOUSE
76. TILES
77. PITCHER
78. THRICE
79. KIJGAF
80. BFCAJGF
81. 6  4  7  2  **
82. 4  2  7  6  **
83. 4  2  7  6  **
84. 7  4  2  6  **
85. 4  6  7  2  **

*   There are other possibilities.
**  Other combinations may work.

These are the answers to Book 2 of a set of 4 graded books. A child who has not previously attempted questions of this type may have difficulty with the first few tests. However, research shows that a child's ability to handle and understand these questions generally increases with practice.

website: www.learningtogether.co.uk     E-mail: info@learningtogether.co.uk     Learning Together, 23 Carlston Avenue Holywood Co Down BT18 ONF     Phone/Fax 028 90425852/028 90402086

# Answers to Test 08

1. H
2. H
3. D
4. DIFFICULT    TEACHER
5. THUNDER    THE
6. DOG'S    RACED
7. BOOK    FIVE
8. TO    SOMETIMES
9. SLEEP    TIME
10. B, G, M or T
11. K or T
12. L
13. S
14. Y
15. H
16. 0.4
17. 11.3
18. 7.3
19. 13.1
20. 6
21. 26
22. 389
23. 39
24. 62
25. 39
26. BOAR
27. FORE or REAR
28. HIVE
29. MINT
30. AUNT
31. HERE
32. YEAR or EARN
33. CHAPTER
34. BORING
35. DEVELOPED
36. RESCUED
37. HELPLESS
38. 560
39. 952
40. £1.75
41. £3
42. PENGUIN
43. SHOULDER
44. VARNISH
45. MANHOLE
46. RUCKSACK
47. FAITHFUL
48. EVIDENCE
49. 5
50. 20th
51. MONDAY
52. 27th
53. 12th
54. 19
55. 162
56. 3.5
57. 6.4
58. 6.87
59. £12.50
60. £3.49
61. £1.70
62. YES
63. 8
64. 23
65. 3
66. 1/5
67. SW
68. SW
69. NE
70. NW
71. WIND
72. BLOOD
73. POST
74. MAN
75. LAND
76. TOM
77. RUTH
78. BETTY
79. TOM
80. E
81. D
82. B
83. F
84. A
85. C

# Answers to Test 09

1. E
2. E
3. E
4. 16
5. 11
6. THE    WHY
7. ITS    HORSE
8. OUT    WHEN
9. BASKET    LOT
10. INTO    RODE
11. EAT    SIT
12. 1.9
13. 7.7
14. 8.9
15. 5
16. 6
17. T
18. K
19. R or T
20. H
21. T
22. R
23. POCKET
24. POETRY
25. POPPET
26. POPPY
27. PUPPY
28. GAVE    SLING
29. FOND    BUOY
30. SHOT    BEARD/BREAD
31. DEER    STING
32. FLAT    SHOUT
33. RISE    SNAIL
34. TILE    STACK
35. IR
36. Y
37. P
38. NRN
39. OMN
40. OEK
41. ROY
42. BOB
43. 7
44. 1997
45. 7 or 7½
46. SEEDS
47. TENDED
48. ESSENTIAL
49. INSUFFICIENT
50. HAMPER
51. A
52. C
53. PAINTING
54. B
55. C
56. FOOTBALL
57. LIME    LINE    *
58. WEAR    TEAR    *
59. PACE    RACE    *
60. PANT    PANE    *
61. WORD    LORD    *
62. 3    SQ ROOT X-2
63. 38    2X+6
64. 122    X SQUARED + 1
65. 17    HALF X-3
66. 41    SQUARED X-2
67. 34    2X - 10
68. 8
69. 3
70. 3
71. 7
72. 1
73. SLAIN    PULSE
74. GRAPE    REPAY
75. CHASE    HEARD
76. TULIP    LAMENT
77. BLAME    UNCLE
78. ROAST    TREAT
79. FUEDS    URGES
80. 2
81. 5 and 9
82. 4 and 7
83. 52
84. 11
85. 3

# Answers to Test 10

1. O
2. M
3. N and G
4. 14
5. 5
6. FROM    TEAR
7. PARK    RODE
8. COULD    FUSED
9. DOOR    SEE
10. CURLY    MOST
11. BOOKS    MARKED
12. 2.8
13. 11.3
14. 8.5
15. 1.8
16. 3.4
17. 3.7
18. K
19. E
20. S
21. R
22. T
23. U
24. BOW    LED
25. GO    AT
26. ARM    OUR
27. OR    BIT
28. ME    AN
29. PIE    AN
30. TIE    BALD
31. SERVE    HEARD
32. HOT    TWIN
33. FIGHT    SEVEN or EVENS
34. BLOW    LAST
35. BAD
36. BIN
37. HOT
38. ROB
39. PAN
40. HAT
41. TRAINERS, WELLINGTON
42. FRY, ROAST
43. TORCH, MATCH
44. UNHAPPY, DREARY
45. IRIS, ROSE
46. 6
47. 1
48. 4
49. 3
50. 2
51. B
52. 4
53. 3
54. 3
55. 2
56. ROOF
57. WATER
58. ENGINE
59. LIMBS
60. 5
61. TUESDAY
62. 11th
63. JANUARY
64. 4
65. DOT
66. EDITH
67. EDITH
68. BETH
69. AMY
70. WARM    WORM    *
71. TIME    TILE    *
72. MANE    MINE    *
73. SANK    BANK    *
74. CARD    CARE    *
75. LOST    LAST    *
76. 65    X CUBED + 1
77. 43    6X + 1
78. 22    (X ÷ 3) + 2
79. 10    SQ ROOT X + 1
80. 24    5 X - 1
81. 86    REVERSE NUM-BERS
82. 40 KM
83. 40 KM/H
84. 100 KM
85. 12.00 O'CLOCK

*THERE ARE OTHER POSSIBILITIES